The Complete Praise Christmas Keyboard Player

Paul Douglas & Dean Austin

MOORLEY'S Print & Publishing
23 Park Rd., Ilkeston, Derbys DE7 5DA
Tel/Fax: (0115) 932 0643

ISBN 0 86071 483 7

Cover Design: John Moorley
Notation: Dean Austin
Typesetting: Moorley's Print & Publishing

WELCOME TO THE COMPLETE PRAISE CHRISTMAS KEYBOARD PLAYER !

Following on from the success of the first two Complete Praise Keyboard Player Books, we have answered your requests for more, and hope that this collection of Christmas music will keep you busy for a while....

Once again, the songs are graded, so that by the end of the book the rhythms and chords are a lot more complex than those at the start.

This publication is part of the growing "Complete Praise" series, which came about as a result of our commitment to make worship songs accessible to the current generation of emerging musicians.

Other titles in the series: The Complete Praise Keyboard Player, Book 1

The Complete Praise Keyboard Player, Book 2

The Complete Praise Piano Player.

We hope you enjoy playing the blend of traditional and contemporary songs this Christmas, or whenever your want to play them.

Paul Douglas B.Mus.(Hons.)
Dean Austin B.Mus.(Hons.)
Directors, Pawprint Music September 1996

CONTENTS

WHILE SHEPHERDS WATCHED

suggested voice : trombone
rhythm : rock
tempo : medium (♩ = *104*)

Words & Music by
Nahum Tate

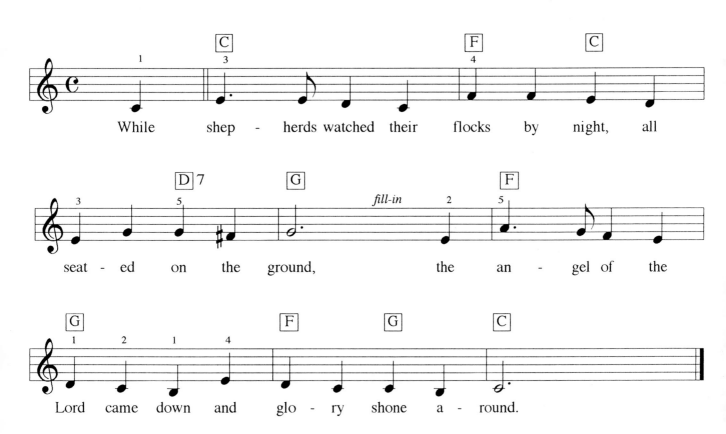

SILENT NIGHT
(Stille Nacht)

suggested voice : flute
rhythm : waltz
tempo : medium (♩ = *110*)

Words by Joseph Mohr
Music by Franz Gruber

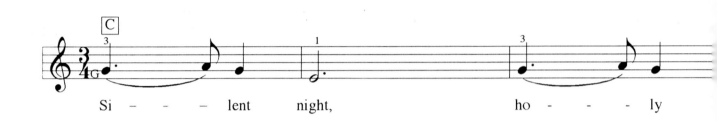

Si – – – lent night, ho – – ly

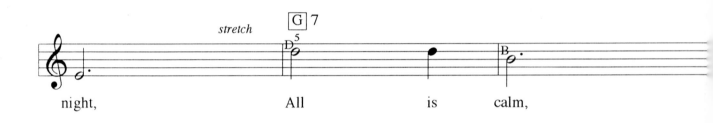

night, All is calm,

all is bright. Round yon

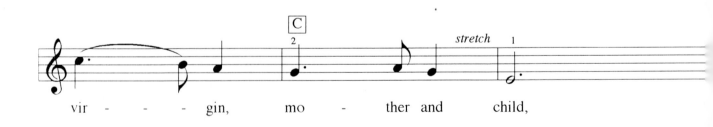

vir – – – gin, mo – ther and child,

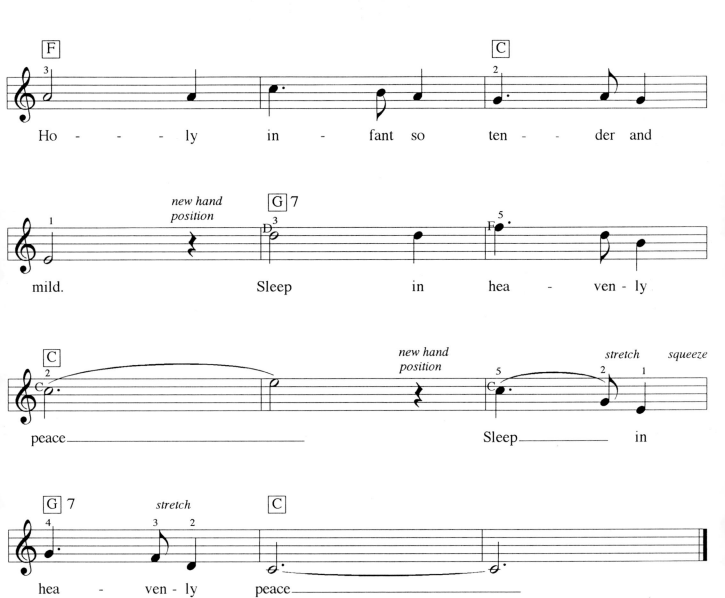

Ho - - - ly in - fant so ten - - der and mild. Sleep in hea - ven - ly peace_____ Sleep_____ in hea - ven - ly peace_____

SUSSEX CAROL

suggested voice : oboe
rhythm: waltz
tempo : fast (♩ = *150*)

English
traditional
carol

BORN IN THE NIGHT

suggested voice : horn
rhythm : pop ballad
tempo : medium slow (♩ = 90)

Words & Music by
Geoffrey Ainger

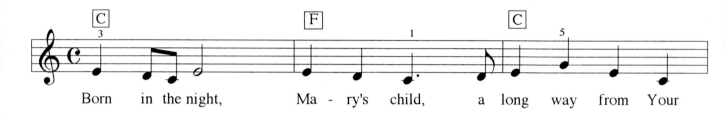

Born in the night, Ma - ry's child, a long way from Your

home _____ com - ing in need, Ma - ry's child,

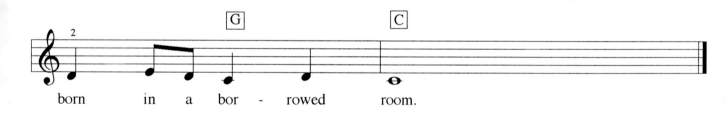

born in a bor - rowed room.

GIVE US LOVE
(excerpt)

suggested voice: vibes
rhythm: 8 beat
tempo: medium

Words & Music by
G. Hauser / A.P. Douglas

FIRST PART

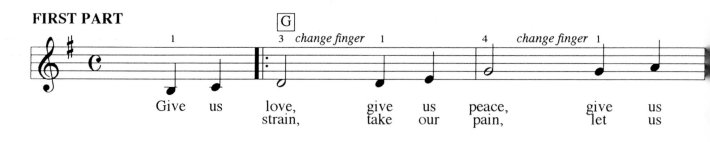

Give us love,   give us peace,   give us
strain,   take our pain,   let us

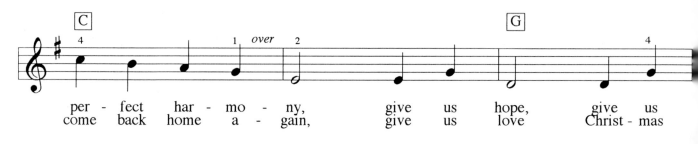

per - fect har - mo - ny,   give us hope,   give us
come back home a - gain,   give us love   Christ - mas

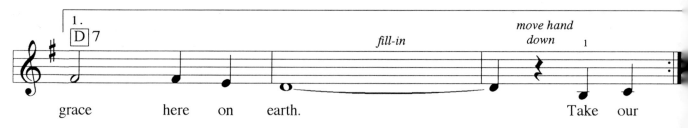

grace here on earth.   Take our

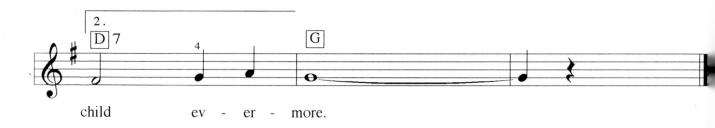

child   ev - er - more.

A recording of this song appears on the C.D. "FREE SOME DAY" by Paul Douglas
-available from Pawprint Music or from all good Christian bookshops.

SECOND PART

You know it's in the seas - on

so let us know the reas - on, for our

light and hope to-day — are so real.

All the stain of liv - ing and the pain that we're

— in The Christ- mas child can

heal.

We would suggest that a teacher could play the second part
as a duet, or perhaps pre-record it into the keyboard.

11.

AWAY IN A MANGER

suggested voice : horn
rhythm : waltz (or accomp. off)
tempo : medium slow   (♩ = *100*)

Melody by
W.J. Kirkpatrick

THE FIRST NOWELL

suggested voice : strings
rhythm : slow waltz
tempo : medium slow ($\quarternote = 100$)

Words & Music :
traditional

JOY TO THE WORLD

suggested voice : string ensemble
rhythm : classic rock/march
tempo : medium fast (♩ = *120*)

Words by I. Watts
Music by G.F. Handel

LITTLE DONKEY

suggested voice : clarinet
rhythm : bossa nova
tempo : medium (♩ = *110*)

Words & Music :
traditional

Li - tle don - key, lit- tle don - key on the dus - ty
road. Lit- tle don - key, car- ry Ma - ry,
with her pre - cious load. Ring out those
bells to - night, Beth - le - hem, Beth - le - hem.
Sing out the news to - night,
Beth - le - hem, Beth - le - hem.

THE CHRISTMAS CHILD

suggested voice : pan flute

rhythm : soul

tempo : medium fast (♩ = *130*)

Words & Music by
Grahan Kendrick

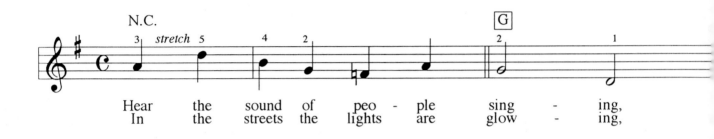

Hear the sound of peo - ple sing - ing,
In the streets the lights are glow - ing,

all the bells are ring - ing for the Christ - mas
but there is no know - ing of the Christ - mas

child. _____ Oh, _____
child. _____

_____ let this Child be born in your heart, _____

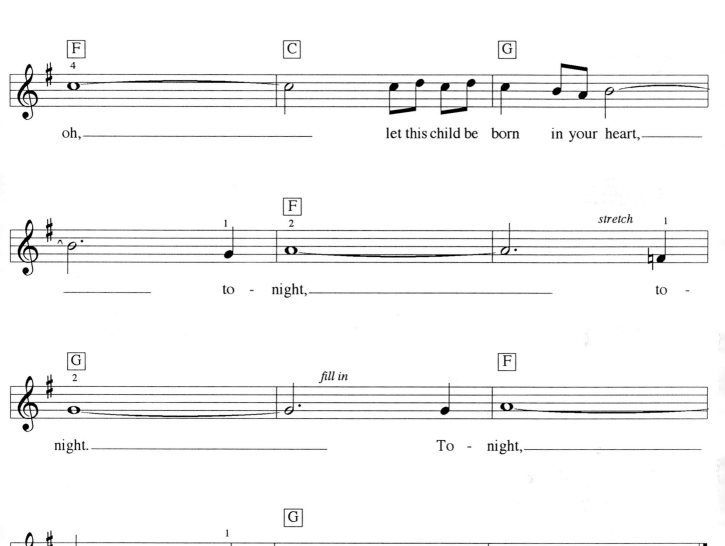

oh,_____ let this child be born in your heart,____

_____ to - night,_____ to -

night._____ To - night,_____

_____ to - night._____

SEE AMID THE WINTER'S SNOW

suggested voice : oboe
rhythm : bossa nova
tempo : medium (♩ = 110)

Words by E. Caswall
Music by J. Goss

CRADLED IN A MANGER

suggested voice : clarinet
rhythm : waltz
tempo : medium (♩ = *100*)

Words by G.S. Rave
Music by S.J.P. Dunman

WE THREE KINGS

suggested voice : accordion
rhythm : waltz
tempo : medium ($\quad$ = 120)

Words & Music by
J.H. Hopkins

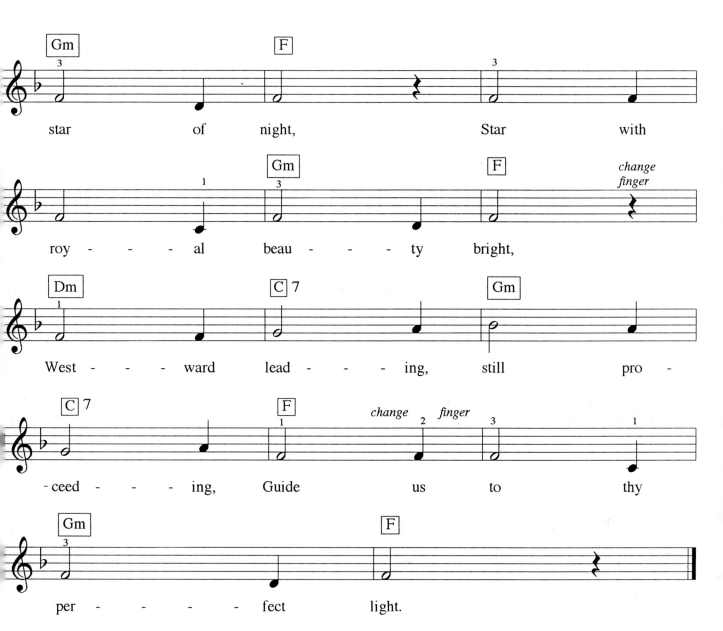

star   of   night,   Star   with

roy - - - al   beau - - - ty   bright,

West - - - ward   lead - - - ing,   still   pro -

- ceed - - - ing,   Guide   us   to   thy

per - - - - - fect   light.

O COME, ALL YE FAITHFUL

suggested voice : violin
rhythm : rock/pop
tempo : medium (♩ = *116*)

Words by F. Oakley
Music by J.F. Wade

GOOD CHRISTIAN MEN, REJOICE

suggested voice : electric guitar
rhythm : 8beat pop
tempo : fast (♩ = *140*)

words: 14th. Cent.
Music by Dean Austin

HARK! THE HERALD ANGELS SING

suggested voice : trumpet
rhythm : soul
tempo : medium (♩ = *100*)

Words by Wesley,
Whitefield, Madan & others
Music by Mendelssohn

IN THE BLEAK MID-WINTER

suggested voice : flute
rhythm : ballad
tempo : fairly slow (♩ = 85)

Words by C.G. Rossetti
Music by G. Holst

THE VIRGIN MARY HAD A BABY BOY

suggested voice : steel drum
rhythm : reggae/samba
tempo : medium fast   (♩ = 120)

Words & Music:
traditional

The vir - gin Ma - ry had a ba - by boy___ The

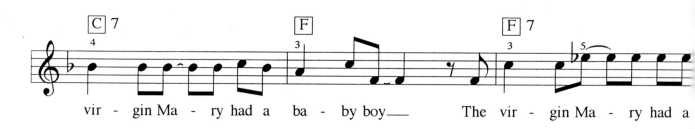

vir - gin Ma - ry had a ba - by boy___ The vir - gin Ma - ry had a

ba - by boy___ and they say that his name was Je - sus.

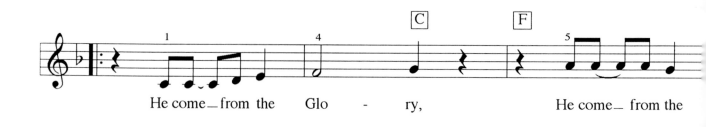

He come__ from the Glo - ry, He come__ from the

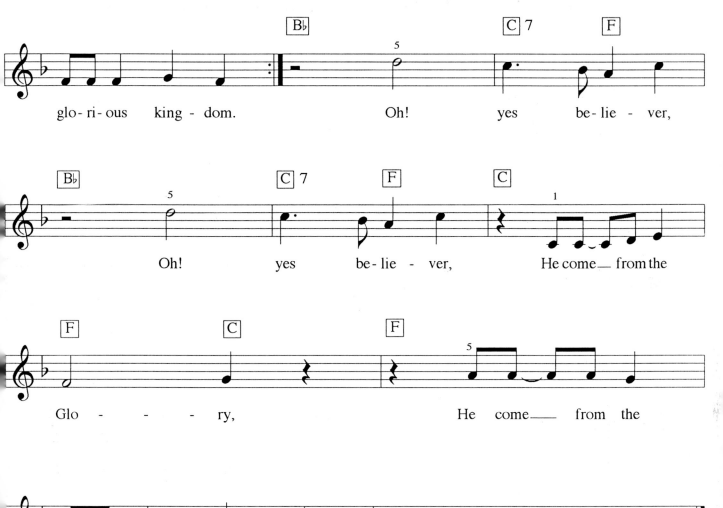

glo-ri-ous king-dom. Oh! yes be-lie-ver,

Oh! yes be-lie-ver, He come— from the

Glo - - - ry, He come— from the

glo - ri - ous king - dom.

HE WALKED WHERE I WALK
(GOD WITH US)

suggested voice : rock organ
rhythm : hard rock
tempo : medium fast (♩ = *130*)

Words and Music by
Graham Kendrick

HEAVEN INVITES YOU TO A PARTY
(excerpt)

suggested voice : trumpet
rhythm : hard rock
tempo : fast   (♩ = 120)

Words & Music by
Graham Kendrick

IMMANUEL, O IMMANUEL

suggested voice : strings
rhythm : pop ballad
tempo : medium (♩ = *120*)

Words & Music by
Graham Kendrick

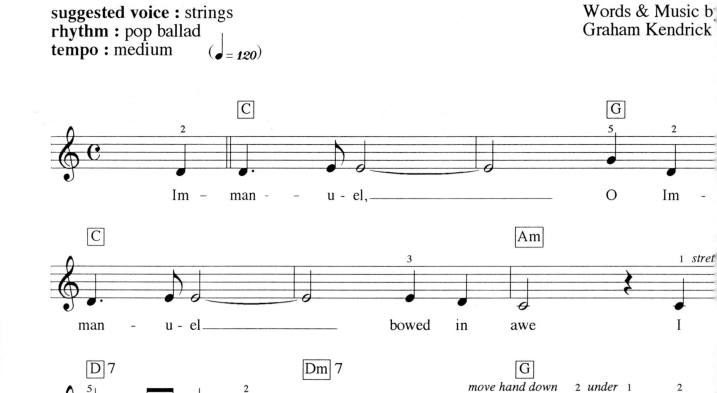

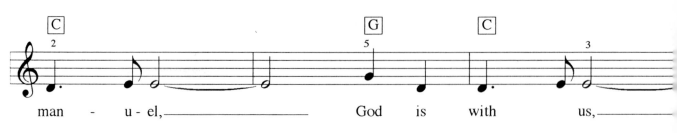

weak - ness-es,———— my pain, tak - ing the pun - ish-ment,——— the
heart can-not——— con - tain, great are the glo - ries of——— Your

blame, Im - man - u - el.——————————— And now my

name, Im - man - - - -

— — — — u - el.

WHAT CHILD IS THIS?

suggested voice : alto sax.
rhythm : slow waltz
tempo : medium slow (♩ = *100*)

Words : traditional
Music by Dean Austi

O LITTLE TOWN OF BETHLEHEM

suggested voice : trumpet
rhythm : 8 beat
tempo : medium (♩ = **120**)

Words by P. Brocks
Music : traditional

LO, HE COMES
WITH CLOUDS DESCENDING

suggested voice : pipe organ
rhythm : rock
tempo : triumphantly! (♩ = 76)

Words by C. Wesley
Music by A.P. Dougla

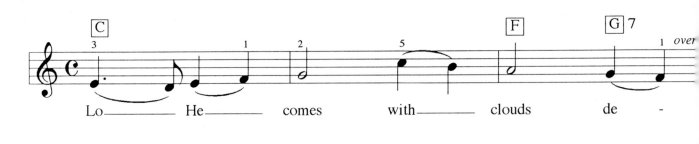

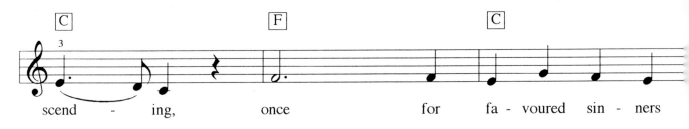

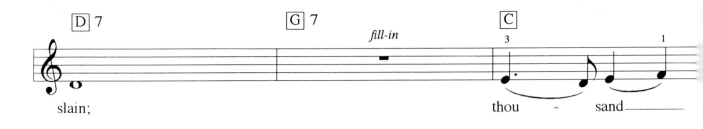

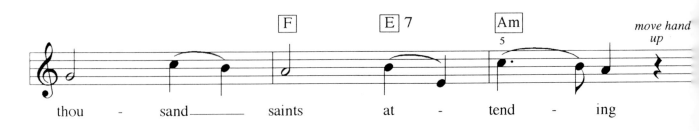

swell   the ____ tri - umph ____ of   His ____

train;   Hal - - - le - lu - jah!

Hal - - - le - lu - jah! ____ God   ap -

-pears   on   earth   to   reign ____

35.

COME AND JOIN THE CELEBRATION

suggested voice : accordion
rhythm : rock & roll/swing
tempo : fast

Words & Music by
Valerie Collison

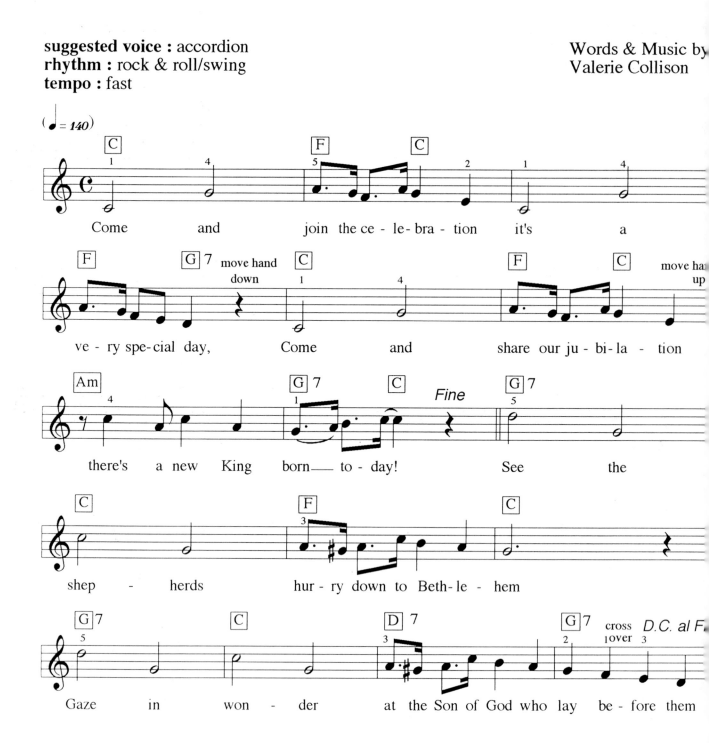

SEE HIM LYING ON A BED OF STRAW

suggested voice : marimba
rhythm : calypso/samba
tempo : fairly fast   (♩ = 126)

Words & Music by
M. Perry

HAIL TO THE KING!

suggested voice: oboe
rhythm : pop ballad
tempo : medium slow (♩ = *90*)

Words and Music by
Dave Middleton

A child is born / The light of the world
A son is / He lights our

gi - ven / dark - ness
in man - ger bare / the Son of God

1. in swadd - ling bands.
2. God's gift to

men. Hail to the King! lay-ing

in the arms of Ma - ry, Hail to the

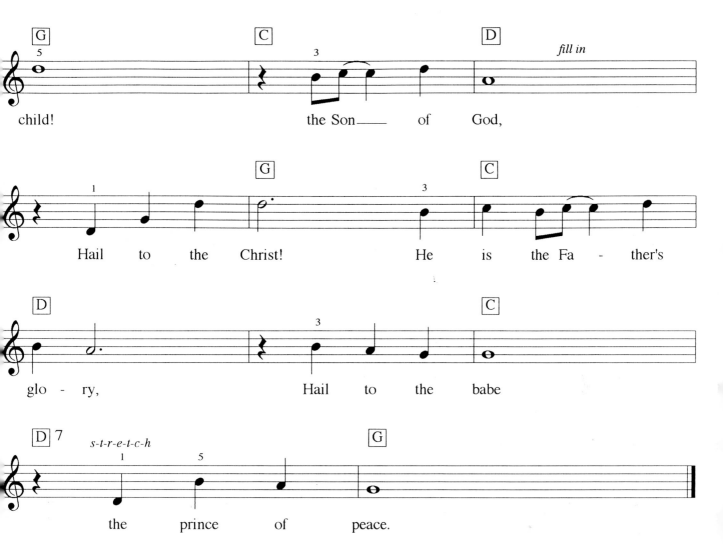

child!   the Son___ of   God,

Hail   to   the   Christ!   He   is   the Fa - ther's

glo - ry,   Hail   to   the   babe

the   prince   of   peace.

MOORLEY'S

are growing Publishers,
adding several new titles to our list each
year. We also undertake private
publications and commissioned works.

**Our range of publications
includes: Books of Verse**
        Devotional Poetry
        Recitations
        Drama
        Bible Plays
        Sketches
        Nativity Plays
        Passiontide Plays
        Easter Plays
        Demonstrations
        Resource Books
        Assembly Material
        Songs & Musicals
        Children's Addresses
        Prayers & Graces
        Daily Readings
        Books for Speakers
        Activity Books
        Quizzes
        Puzzles
        Painting Books
        Daily Readings
        Church Stationery
        Notice Books
        Cradle Rolls
        Hymn Board Numbers

Please send a S.A.E. (approx 9" x 6") for the
current catalogue or consult your local Christian
Bookshop who should stock or be able to order
our titles.